11+
English
Spelling & Vocabulary

Advanced Level
WORKBOOK 10

Stephen C. Curran

with Warren Vokes

Edited by Mark Schofield

This book belongs to

Accelerated Education Publications Ltd.

uniform	perform	force
skull	utmost	expense
expensive	relative	standard
scholar	ninety	safety

Exercise 206a

1) The hotel is **situated** within the medieval walls of the old town.

2) There are many athletes who *perform* best under pressure.

3) The two minute silence began as Big Ben struck eleven *o'clock* .

4) It is an old adage that states that there is *safety* in numbers.

5) He preserved his integrity at the *expense* of his job.

6) The glider continued to *soar* high in the air on the rising thermals.

7) The first half was *expensive* for the home team who conceded three goals.

8) A year can be divided into quarters; each being approximately *ninety* days.

9) All the items were manufactured to a *uniform* standard.

10) "I'll bring you up a mug of *cocoa* before you go to sleep." **Score** 10

Exercise 206b

11) 'High *force* ' takes its name from the Northern England word for waterfall.

12) Everyone wore *period* costume for the re-enactment of the historic battle.

13) A sign depicting the *skull* and crossbones is used as a symbol of danger or death.

14) The *standard* gauge is used for most public railway systems around the world.

15) "I thought you two knew each other: *surely* you've met before."

16) Their voices were drowned out by the *roar* of the wind and the waves.

17) She did her *utmost* to persuade him to change his mind.

18) The percentage of water vapour in the air is expressed as the *relative* humidity.

19) "I'm not *entirely* sure that you were not involved in this prank!"

20) She is a keen *scholar*, with a hunger for knowledge. **Score** 10

2

surely	**entirely**
o'clock	**period**
roar	**soar**
cocoa	**situated**

Word Bank TOTAL 4,120

Across

206

1. At the most distant point or extremity.
3. To fly or rise high in the air.
7. Definitely or unavoidably.
9. An unsweetened brown powder made from roasted and ground beans, used in making chocolate, in cooking, and as the base for a hot drink.
10. To carry out an action or accomplish a task.
11. An interval of time.
13. The skeletal part of the head in humans and other vertebrates.
15. The power, strength or energy that somebody or something possesses.
17. Measured or considered in comparison with each other or with something else.
18. Somebody who has a great deal of knowledge, especially an academic who specializes in a particular arts subject.
19. The cardinal number 90.

Down

2. Protection from, or non exposure to, the risk of harm or injury.
4. To make a loud, natural growling noise.
5. In every sense.
6. The level of quality or excellence attained by somebody or something.
7. Located in the place or position.
8. The amount of money spent in order to buy or do something.
12. Costing a lot of money.
14. A distinctive set of clothes worn to identify somebody's occupation, affiliation or status.
16. In telling the time, used to indicate an exact hour of the day or night.

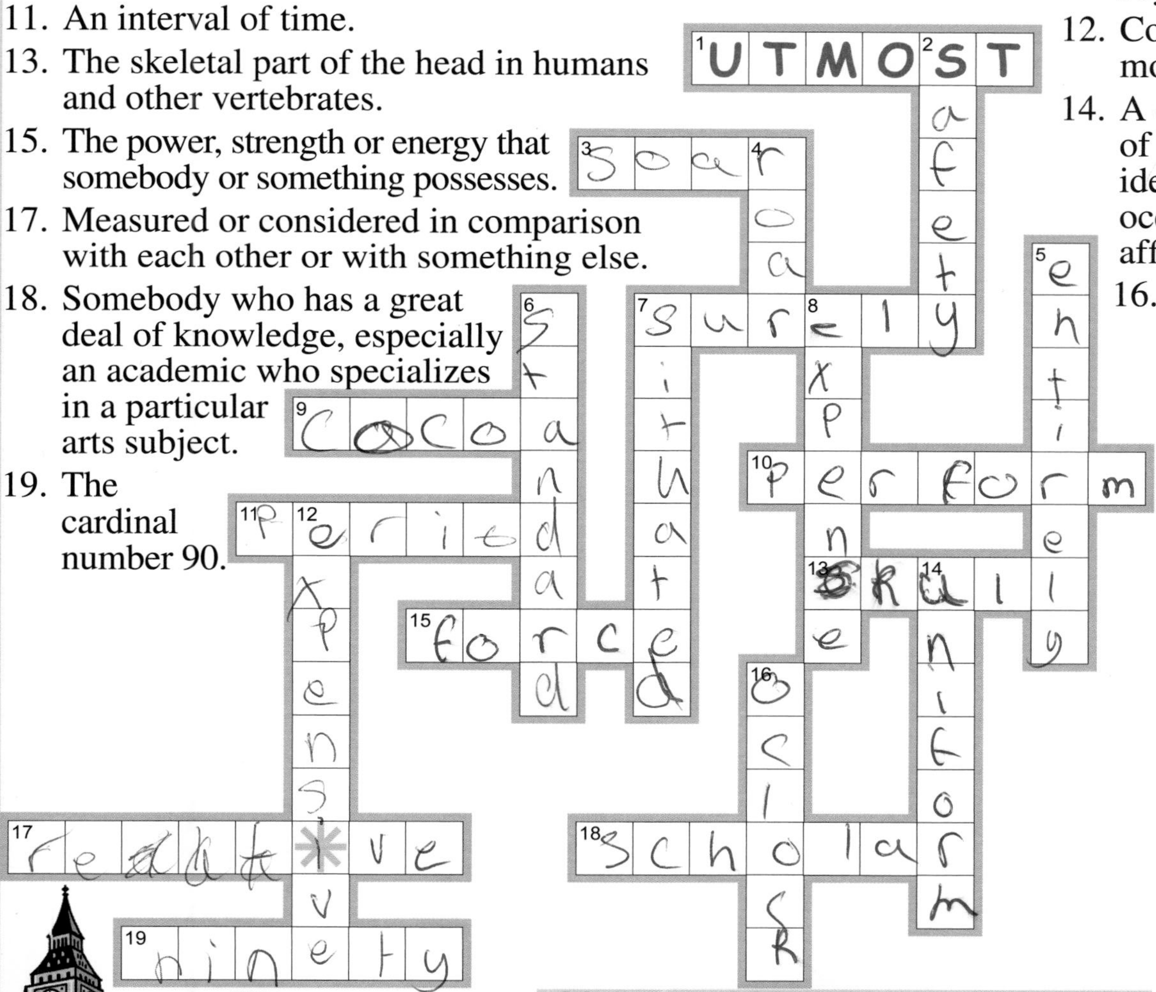

Put the mystery letter (✳) into the box marked **206** below. Add in the mystery letters from puzzles **207** to **212** and then rearrange them to make **Oliver's Mystery Word**. The clue is **COUNTRY**.

206	207	208	209	210	211	212

Mystery Word:

Now rearrange them:

Score /20

general   generally   practical
natural   naturally   embrace
surface   furnace   wasp
sleepiness   threat   weapon

Across

207

2. The condition of being heavy.
4. To release air through the windpipe and mouth sharply and noisily.
5. In most cases or circumstances.
6. A unit of weight equal to one-sixteenth of a pound in the avoirdupois system.
8. A liquid food made by cooking meat, fish, vegetables and other ingredients in water, milk or stock.
10. As might be expected.
12. A device designed to inflict injury or death on an opponent.
14. The top part of the face above the eyebrows.
16. Not specific, detailed, or clearly defined.

Across (continued)

17. The outermost or uppermost part of a thing that can be seen and touched.
19. The feeling of being drowsy and wanting to sleep.

Down

1. The expression of a deliberate intention to cause harm or pain.
3. Happening once a year.
7. Relating to nature.
9. Concerned with actual facts and experience, not theory.
11. A company or other organization that buys and sells goods, makes products, or provides services.
13. The feeling of being tired, especially in having run out of strength, patience, or endurance.
14. An enclosure in which heat is produced by burning fuel.
15. To hug somebody in your arms fondly.
18. A slender, black-and-yellow striped, social stinging insect.

VIVE LA FRANCE!

Mystery Letter

Score

/20

| forehead | heaviness |
| w...
weariness	annual
cough	ounce
soup	business

forehead   heaviness
weariness   annual
cough   ounce
soup   business

Word Bank
TOTAL
4,140

Exercise 207a

1) People seldom act _____ when being videoed.

2) A new committee was elected at the club's _____ general meeting.

3) A general aura of _____ hung over the quiet, remote little village.

4) The forecast indicates a _____ of severe thunderstorms.

5) She saw the cormorant dive beneath the water and _____ with a fish.

6) Domestic appliances were converted to burn _____ gas instead of town gas.

7) The _____ of a diver's weighted boots keeps him upright underwater.

8) He played a _____ joke on his brother who failed to be amused.

9) The operation was performed under a _____ anaesthetic.

10) Iron ore is smelted in a blast _____ to produce pig iron. **Score** ◻ 10

Exercise 207b

11) Earth first consisted of a primordial _____ of hydrogen, oxygen and other gases.

12) The first nuclear _____ was used against Japan to end World War II.

13) His niggling _____ was making his throat sore and annoying his family.

14) He fell in the playground and cut his _____ just above his left eye.

15) "Anyone with an _____ of common sense would take an umbrella today!"

16) She discovered the nest by watching a _____ fly under the eaves and into the loft.

17) He had been toiling all day and he was overcome with _____ .

18) In her work as an aid worker she learnt to _____ a whole new way of life.

19) He spoke _____ about his life but without much detail.

20) "What _____ is it of yours? I can do what I like!" **Score** ◻ 10

ae © 2006 Stephen Curran

5

bicycle	biscuit	juice
statement	improvement	permission
admission	million	region
union	orphan	geography

Exercise 208a

1) "I'm sorry we quarrelled. I've brought you some flowers as a _____ offering."

2) He completed his _____ of ten years and was released from prison.

3) She lost the case but her lawyers said she would _____ .

4) Between 1918 and 1920 at least 40 _____ people died from 'Spanish Flu'.

5) The exam result showed an _____ in her knowledge and ability.

6) The campaign was successful and raised in the _____ of £15,000.

7) "Would you like a _____ ? I have Bourbons, digestives or custard creams."

8) The British penal _____ of New South Wales, Australia was settled in 1788.

9) She had the headteacher's _____ to be absent from the lesson.

10) She squeezed lemon _____ and sprinkled sugar on her pancake. **Score** ⬜ 10

Exercise 208b

11) He became an _____ at an early age when his parents were killed in an accident.

12) The _____ is a popular mode of transport, especially in India and China.

13) The island is rich in resources and has an _____ supply of food.

14) The layout of his new school seemed strange but he soon learnt its _____ .

15) She was falsely accused and her daughter leapt to her _____ .

16) _____ of guilt was the only option when confronted with new evidence.

17) The trade _____ officials negotiated with the management for improved rates of pay.

18) He carefully reconciled his bank _____ with his chequebook records.

19) The deer was killed _____ when struck by the lorry.

20) The _____ is the largest living land animal. **Score** ⬜ 10

6

Across

208

1. Agreement to allow something to happen or be done.
5. An earnest or urgent request to somebody for something.
6. A country or area that is ruled by another country.
8. Present in great quantities.
10. A thousand thousand.
11. The act of joining together people or things to form a whole.
14. The extractable liquid that is contained in fruit and vegetables.
17. A large grey or greyish-brown animal with a long flexible trunk, prominent ears, thick legs and pointed tusks.
18. A vehicle with two wheels and a seat that is moved by pushing pedals with the feet.
19. A specially prepared announcement or reply that is made in public.
20. A group of words or a single word that expresses a complete thought, feeling, or idea.

Down

2. A change or addition that makes something better.
3. A large land area that has particular geographic, political, or cultural characteristics that distinguish it from others.
4. Immediately and without delay.
7. The study of all the Earth's physical features.
9. A small, flat, dry cake that is usually sweet and crisp.

Down (continued)

12. The protection of something, especially from attack by an enemy.
13. The right, ability, or permission to enter.
15. A child whose parents are both dead, or has been abandoned by his or her parents.
16. Freedom from war, or the time when war or conflict ends.

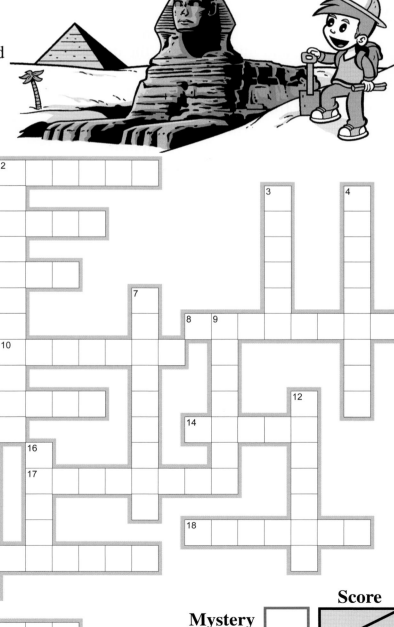

Mystery Letter

Score /20

author	governor	conductor
scent	scene	August
autumn	fault	pause
laundry	brief	priest

Across

209

1. A division of an act of a play.
2. A member of a governing body of an institution.
3. The set or decorated background for a play, film, or opera.
8. To stop doing before carrying on.
10. Characterized by, or showing, aggression or anger.
12. An ordained minister responsible for administering the sacraments, preaching, and ministering to the needs of the congregation.
13. The distance or measurement along something from end to end.
14. To perform the arithmetical calculation of deducting one number or quantity from another.
17. Dirty clothes or linen put aside to be washed and ironed.
18. To hand something in or put something forward for consideration, approval, or judgment.

Down

1. To make a loud, high-pitched piercing sound.
4. A substance, body, or medium that allows heat, electricity, light or sound to pass along or through it.
5. The eighth month of the year in the Gregorian calendar.
6. Lasting for only a short time.
7. An act of looking at or inspecting something.
9. Somebody who writes a book or other text.

Down (continued)

11. The distance or measurement from the top of something to its bottom, from front to back, or from the outside in.
14. A distinctive odour, especially a pleasant one.
15. The season occurring between summer and winter.
16. A responsibility for a mistake, failure, or act of wrongdoing.

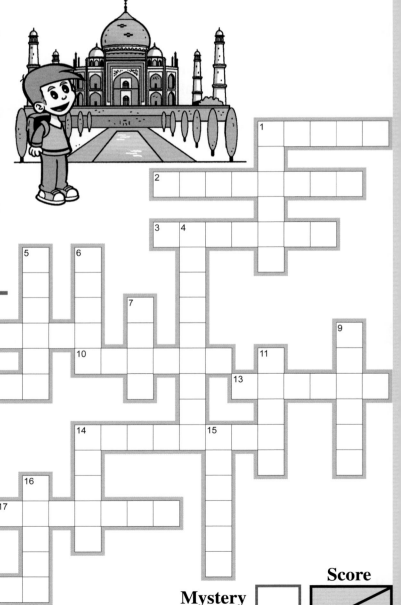

Mystery Letter

Score

20

shriek   fierce
view   scenery
length   depth
submit   subtract

Word Bank TOTAL 4,180

Exercise 209a

1) He has a job in an industrial _____ that washes and cleans overalls.

2) The _____ of the bay was impressive from their vantage point.

3) _____ begins with the sun in the sign of Leo and ends in the sign of Virgo.

4) She had to _____ to extensive examinations before the diagnosis was confirmed.

5) He ran the entire _____ of the rugby pitch to score the try.

6) Buses used to have a _____ to collect the fares.

7) She saw a mouse and gave an involuntary _____ of surprise.

8) He is a famous _____ with seven best-sellers to his name.

9) Many Roman Catholics were hidden in _____ -holes to avoid persecution.

10) The competition was _____ but she won first prize.

Score ⟋ 10

Exercise 209b

11) The stage hands worked tirelessly to change the _____ between acts.

12) He exhibited an incredible _____ of knowledge about the subject.

13) The tracker dogs picked up the _____ and pursued the fugitive.

14) The break in the continuity of the rocks could be seen on either side of the _____ line.

15) A centrifugal _____ uses proportional control to regulate a shaft speed.

16) "Before the play starts, I'll set the _____ and tell you about the characters."

17) The receptionist had failed to _____ the deposit from the final bill.

18) There was a brief _____ in the proceedings and he slipped out unnoticed.

19) Most trees' leaves turn from green to brown in the _____ .

20) She wore a very _____ top that left her midriff exposed.

Score ⟋ 10

choice	rejoice	avoid
moisture	palm	curious
various	glorious	anxious
worthy	arouse	trousers

Exercise 210a

1) He was _____ to make a good first impression at the interview.

2) The X-ray showed that his _____ were fine, with no sign of tuberculosis.

3) The driver reacted immediately but he could not _____ the oncoming vehicle.

4) He had played football in the playground and torn the knee of his _____ .

5) His mother shook his arm to _____ him from a deep sleep.

6) The plants in the greenhouse began to _____ and die.

7) She had to _____ her old passport before being issued with a new one.

8) There are _____ exhibits from that era on display in the museum.

9) He went to a theme park as a _____ treat for his birthday.

10) He climbed the _____ tree and threw down the coconuts.

Score [/10]

Exercise 210b

11) His manner was very _____ and he made no effort to be friendly.

12) The witness supplied vital new evidence that was _____ to the case.

13) Debris was scattered far and wide in the wake of the tornado's _____ .

14) The _____ between the carpet and the wall was quality parquet flooring.

15) The _____ in the bathroom had caused mould to grow on the tiles.

16) "There are several _____ circumstances relating to her cat's disappearance."

17) It was a _____ summer's day: they decided to spend it at the seaside.

18) "Don't worry about writing off your car: _____ in the fact that you weren't injured."

19) She played very well and was a _____ champion.

20) The range offers a wide _____ of styles and colours.

Score [/10]

ae

Across

210

1. Fully deserving something.
5. The paired spongy respiratory organs, situated inside the rib cage.
7. To evoke a feeling, response, or desire.
9. Eager to know about something or to get information.
11. To occupy the space all around something.
13. The inner surface of the hand.
15. A garment for the lower body that covers the area from the waist to the ankles and has separate tube shaped sections for each leg.
16. Many different examples of something.
17. Worried or afraid, especially about something that is going to happen or might happen.
18. The substance used to make things.

Down

1. To shrivel or dry up as part of the process of dying.
2. Beautiful in a way that inspires wonder or joy.
3. Distinct, different, unusual, or superior in comparison to others of the same kind.
4. Being of particularly good quality.
6. Violent anger.
7. To keep away from somebody or something.
8. Sudden and unexpected.
10. To declare to an opponent that he or she has won and that fighting can cease.
12. To feel very happy or show great happiness about something.
14. Wetness, especially droplets of condensed or absorbed liquid, or in a vapour.

Mystery Letter

Score

20

woollen	crooked	loose
foolish	soldier	carriage
marriage	machine	acre
pearl	succeed	success

Across

211

3. Not firmly fastened or fixed in place.

5. To declare that something is not true or not the case.

7. An amount of money, a service, or an item of property that is owed to somebody.

10. Having the intended result.

15. An area regarded as separate or kept separate, especially one with a particular use or function.

16. Relating to the parts of somebody's life that are private.

17. A small, lustrous sphere of calcium carbonate that forms around a grain of sand in a mollusc such as an oyster, and is valued as a gem.

Across (continued)

18. A railway passenger coach.

20. A legally recognized relationship, established by a civil or religious ceremony, between two people who intend to live together as partners.

Down

1. To feel unconvinced or uncertain about something, or think that something is unlikely.

2. Somebody who serves in an army.

4. Something that turns out as planned or attempted.

6. A country comprising North Island and South Island, separated by the Cook Strait.

8. A device with moving parts, often powered by electricity, used to perform a task.

9. To manage to do what is planned or attempted.

11. Sharply curved, bent, or twisted, often in more than one place.

12. A spoken or unspoken communication with God, a deity, or saint.

13. Showing, or resulting from, a lack of good sense or judgment.

14. Knitted or woven using wool.

19. A unit of area equal to 4,840 square yards.

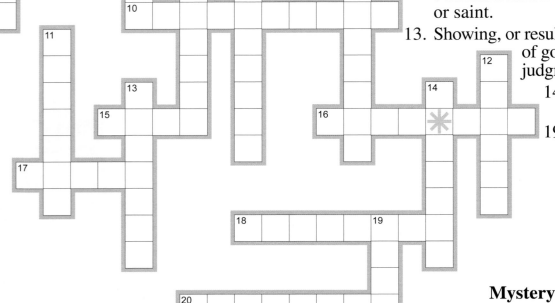

Mystery Letter

Score

20

successful	prayer
deny	New Zealand
zone	debt
doubt	personal

Word Bank TOTAL 4,220

Exercise 211a

1) "I know you're injured but try to _____ on to the end of the game."

2) The house sits on a plot of about one _____ of land in total.

3) The monarch's eldest son will _____ her when she dies.

4) The _____ supporters cheered on the All Blacks rugby team.

5) The waterways authority decided to _____ the canal areas for leisure and recreation.

6) The picture on the wall is _____ and needs to be re-hung.

7) Civilization is based on the _____ of tradition and innovation.

8) She wears thick, knitted _____ gloves to keep her hands warm.

9) The famous actor agreed to make a _____ appearance at the fete.

10) A period of frugality would enable him to clear the _____ .

Score 10

Exercise 211b

11) The play came to the West End after a _____ run in the provinces.

12) "I don't have a _____ of being offered a job overseas, but I'll still apply!"

13) Young _____ fishermen dive to amazing depths to collect oysters.

14) There is little _____ that the poor reversing manoeuvre was the reason he failed.

15) She looked in every shop for a suitable birthday present but without _____ .

16) He dug the heavy, compacted earth while she turned over the lighter _____ soil.

17) He continued to _____ that he was guilty although the evidence was conclusive.

18) She replaced the guitar string and wound it around the _____ head.

19) "Wipe that _____ grin off your face and behave yourself!"

20) The _____ charge seemed excessive for such a small item.

Score 10

ae © 2006 Stephen Curran

13

liberal	festival	removal
criminal	declare	decrease
decline	determine	determination
portion	proportion	production

Exercise 212a

1) The children brought produce into Sunday school for the harvest _____ .

2) The teacher stood at the classroom door to _____ the new pupils.

3) He showed great _____ to lose weight and get fit.

4) The government were returned with a reduced _____ .

5) He helped himself to a _____ helping of apple pie and cream.

6) There was a marked _____ in reservoir levels after two dry winters.

7) The song is sung in a _____ key and sounds very melancholy.

8) Boats taking prisoners to the Tower of London passed through _____ s' Gate.

9) He had been in trouble with the law previously and had a _____ record.

10) The stage _____ received accolades from the critics. **Score** ⬜ 10

Exercise 212b

11) The _____ of lorries to cars on the road has remained the same.

12) The _____ became so steep that he had difficulty keeping his footing.

13) Men were unloading furniture from a _____ van into the house next door.

14) She lay still, trying to _____ what had caused her to wake up with a start.

15) The _____ of tobacco into England is credited to Sir Walter Raleigh.

16) Her parents agreed to _____ her trip to India and the Far East.

17) The captain thought they had scored enough runs and decided to _____ .

18) "How much are you taking? You should have one _____ like everyone else!"

19) A helmet provides _____ from head injuries should a skier fall.

20) The sign warned of _____ roadworks and long delays ahead. **Score** ⬜ 10

Across

212

2. A sum of money invested for a particular purpose.
7. The act of preventing somebody or something from being harmed or damaged.
9. Most of the people or things in a large group.
10. Greater in importance than most others.
13. Somebody who has committed a crime.
14. A part or section of a larger whole.
16. To decide or settle something conclusively.

Across (continued)

18. A quantity of something that is part of the whole amount or number.
19. The process of becoming less, fewer, or smaller.

Down

1. A day or period of celebration, often one of religious significance.
3. Firmness of purpose, will, or intention.
4. A section at the beginning of a book or of another piece of writing.
5. To welcome somebody in a cordial and usually conventional way.
6. To state something in a plain, open, or emphatic way.
8. The taking away or getting rid of something.
11. To give a polite refusal to an invitation.
12. Somebody who behaves in a disloyal or treacherous manner.
14. The making or creation of something.
15. Tolerant of different views and standards of behaviour in others.
17. Relatively small in quantity, size or degree.

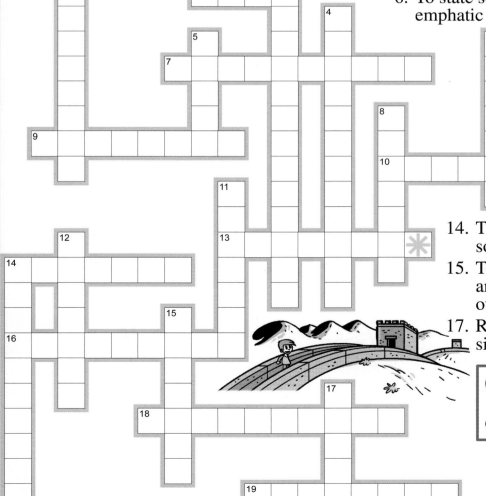

Don't forget to go back to page **3** and complete **Oliver's Mystery Word**.

Mystery Letter

Score

20

15

At the Wedding

Can you find all these words in the picture below? Write the correct word against each number. When you have finished you can colour in the picture if you want to.

candle	posy	pew	arch	bride
angel	bridegroom	bookmark	bow-tie	tapestry
pillar	surplice	choir	bridesmaid	pulpit

1._____   2._____   3._____

4._____   5._____   6._____

7._____   8._____   9._____

10._____   11._____   12._____

13._____   14._____   15._____

At the Visit to HMS Victory

Can you find all these words in the picture below? Write the correct word against each number.

ensign	topsail	cannonball	rigging	jib
rudder	anchor	gangplank	mizzen	barrel
portholes	gaff	crow's-nest	dory	bollard

1._____ 2._____ 3._____

4._____ 5._____ 6._____

7._____ 8._____ 9._____

10._____ 11._____ 12._____

13._____ 14._____ 15._____

Across

213

4. The spirit of somebody who has died, or a frightening atmosphere in a place.
5. To teach somebody a subject or how to do something.
8. The act of adding something onto or into something else.
9. Physical damage to the body or a part of the body.
12. To declare or report something publicly.
13. To confront somebody with a charge of having done something illegal, wrong, or undesirable.
15. To say or do something rude or insensitive that offends somebody else.
16. A job or occupation regarded as a long-term or lifelong activity.
17. To make yourself or somebody else become used to something through frequent or prolonged contact or use.
18. Very eager and willing.
19. The rigid framework of interconnected bones and cartilage.

Down

1. Somebody who operates or services machines.
2. To cause physical hurt or damage to a person, animal, or body part.

Down (continued)

3. A formal or legally binding agreement.
6. A fabric case filled with soft material, used to sit or lean on.
7. A person or group that is the first to do something.
10. A mountainous peninsula between the Mediterranean and Aegean Sea.
11. To put something inside or into something else.
12. Giving a correct or truthful representation of something.
14. The amount of money received over a period of time.

Put the mystery letter (✳) into the box marked **213** below. Add in the mystery letters from puzzles **214** to **220** and then rearrange them to make **Kate's Mystery Word**.
The clue is **FOOTWEAR**.

Mystery Word:

213	214	215	216	217	218	219	220

Now rearrange them:

Score

/20

18   © 2006 Stephen Curran   ae

injure   injury   Word Bank
keen   ghost   TOTAL
skeleton   cushion   4,260
income   contract

Exercise 213a

1) The staff have a _____ key that opens every hotel bedroom.

2) He received a generous pension to _____ the blow of early retirement.

3) Amy Johnson was a _____ aviatrix who flew from England to Australia.

4) We saw the Parthenon and the Acropolis during our holiday in _____ .

5) His solicitor advised him to _____ a barrister to defend him in court.

6) The trumpeters sounded a fanfare to _____ the Queen's arrival.

7) It was an _____ weather forecast and the rain arrived exactly as predicted.

8) It was a _____ wind that chilled them to the marrow.

9) The article was written deliberately to _____ the minister's reputation.

10) They formulated a secret plan to _____ their success. **Score** [/10]

Exercise 213b

11) The _____ train at the fair always scared her although she knew what to expect.

12) He listed his earnings for the year on his _____ - tax return.

13) The railway truck broke away and began to _____ down the track.

14) "Are you going to _____ anyone here of perpetrating the crime?"

15) She agreed the terms, signed the _____ and paid a deposit.

16) He checked in his golf clubs in _____ to two large suitcases.

17) Her knee _____ forced her to withdraw from the team.

18) He trained in Malaysia to _____ his body to high humidity.

19) The apprentice learnt how to _____ pistons into an engine block.

20) The article was an _____ to the reader's intelligence. **Score** [/10]

ae © 2006 Stephen Curran   19

control	consent	contempt
conclude	prefer	preferred
conferred	grudge	lodging
wholesome	enterprise	therefore

Exercise 214a

1) She felt nothing but _____ for the man who had mistreated his dog.

2) Their guide pointed out the _____ where the path crossed the mountain ridge.

3) It is a portable, _____ system that transmits using radio waves.

4) The captain _____ with the team members before answering the question.

5) "It is a serious matter and I would _____ to speak to the manager in person."

6) "I think, _____ I am," is a philosophical statement by René Descartes.

7) She was _____ for the advice that had saved her several hundred pounds.

8) They asked where they might find _____ for the night.

9) Their constant bickering only seemed to _____ their relationship.

10) He failed to _____ the skid and his car hit the railings. **Score** ⟋ 10

Exercise 214b

11) He asked for her father's _____ before he proposed to his fiancée.

12) Oil exploration is a risky _____ but it can yield vast profits.

13) "Don't _____ to call me as soon as you have some more news."

14) A breakfast cereal with a high content of fruit and fibre is _____ .

15) Her husband liked country walks but she _____ to cycle.

16) The evidence was overwhelming and enough to _____ the jury of his guilt.

17) "I wouldn't _____ working late if I knew we could finish the job."

18) She was certain that the novel would _____ with a happy ending.

19) A decision was made to _____ the building as uninhabitable.

20) "She has the patience of Job and the _____ of Solomon." **Score** ⟋ 10

  ae

Across

214

1. Talked to somebody in order to compare opinions or make a decision.
4. Given priority to one person, especially a creditor, over others.
6. To be slow to act in doing something or saying something.
9. A radio or a radio set.
10. A substance that causes illness, injury or death if taken into the body or produced within the body.
14. Beneficial to physical health or to moral wellbeing.
16. A series of connected loops into which something has been wound or gathered.
17. Having the desire or reason to thank somebody.

Across (continued)

18. To state that something or somebody is in some way wrong or unacceptable.
19. To work or operate something such as a vehicle or machine.

Down

1. A powerful feeling of dislike towards somebody or something considered to be worthless, inferior, or undeserving of respect.
2. The knowledge and experience needed to make sensible decisions and judgments.
3. And so, or because of that.
5. A new, often risky, venture that involves confidence and initiative.
7. A feeling of resentment or ill will, especially one lasting a long time.
8. To give permission or approval for something to happen.
11. To form an opinion or make a logical judgment about something after considering everything known about it.
12. Somewhere to stay temporarily.
13. To make somebody sure or certain of something.
15. To like or want one thing more than another.

Mystery Letter | **Score** / 20

delicate   **candidate**   **certificate**
navigate   **continent**   **fragment**
regiment   **experiment**   **cement**
stage   **garage**   **average**

Across

215

5. Packed suitcases and bags.
7. Any one of the seven large continuous land masses that constitute most of the dry land on the surface of the earth.
8. A piece broken off something or left when something is shattered.
11. The level, amount, or degree of something that is typical of a group, or class of people, or things.
12. To talk about something at length and in detail.
15. A fine grey powder of calcined limestone and clay, used to make mortar or concrete.
16. To try to stop somebody from doing something.
17. A test carried out in order to discover whether a theory is correct.

Across (continued)

19. A device for taking photographs.
20. A formal contract or agreement negotiated between countries.

Down

1. Somebody who runs for election to a political office or an official position.
2. Certain of having ability, judgment, and resources needed to succeed.
3. An official document that gives proof and details of something.
4. A raised platform in a hall or auditorium.
6. A building for parking or storing one or more motor vehicles.
9. Somebody who is studying at school, college or university.
10. To find a way through a place, or direct the course of something.
13. Easily damaged or broken.
14. A permanent military unit usually consisting of two or three battalions of ground troops under the command of a colonel.
18. A medication or treatment that cures a disease or disorder, or relieves its symptoms.

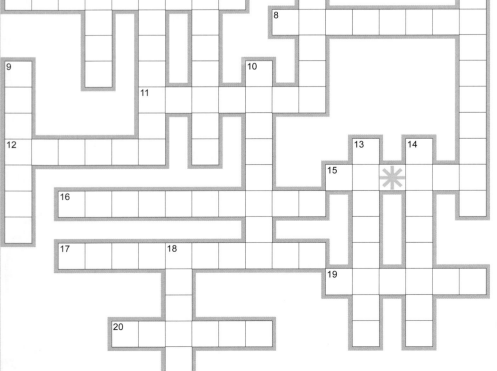

Mystery Letter   **Score**   20

discourage	baggage
debate	student
confident	camera
remedy	treaty

Word Bank
TOTAL
4,300

Exercise 215a

1) "It's a _____ matter and one that needs handling with tact and diplomacy."

2) They are _____ that their product will prove to be popular.

3) The meteorite began to _____ and its energy was dissipated.

4) The results of the first _____ are encouraging but more are required.

5) Many years of working together have served to _____ their relationship.

6) The dirty beaches and lack of facilities _____ holiday makers.

7) The skies are cloudy and it is impossible to _____ using the sextant.

8) The First World War officially ended with the _____ of Versailles in 1919.

9) He tried to _____ the mistake but instead he compounded the problem.

10) She stood as a _____ in the election.

Score [/ 10]

Exercise 215b

11) "There's no time for _____ : we have to decide now!"

12) She was a model _____ and passed all her exams with distinction.

13) He tends to _____ his pupils and stifle their imagination and individuality.

14) The secret meeting was held in _____ , away from media attention.

15) The second _____ exploded and the rocket was completely destroyed.

16) There was no room for a _____ so he erected a carport instead.

17) The airline _____ handlers' strike disrupted flights to and from Heathrow.

18) The company paid higher than the _____ wage for skilled employees.

19) "It is a limited edition print and has a _____ to prove it!"

20) Asia is over 43 million km^2 and is the largest _____ .

Score [/ 10]

23

treatment	ornament	instrument
prominent	lecture	agriculture
temperate	temperature	puncture
nervous	prosperous	tremendous

Exercise 216a

1) Mount St Helens _____ , south of Seattle, erupted catastrophically in 1980.

2) The _____ could not be repaired so he had to buy a new tyre.

3) He asked his secretary to _____ all his calls to his mobile phone.

4) The Petronas Twin Towers are a _____ feature in Kuala Lumpur.

5) Her calmness in the tense situation highlighted her _____ character.

6) The research team kept a _____ guard on their findings.

7) "Come and sit beside me on the _____ and show me your holiday photos."

8) A _____ clap of thunder shook the building.

9) The manuscript's pages were plain and entirely without _____ .

10) Constant stress caused his _____ breakdown.

Score [/ 10]

Exercise 216b

11) Someone had walked passed _____ : wet footprints were still visible.

12) She wore _____ shoes because she knew she would be on her feet all day.

13) He checked the dials on the _____ panel and recorded the readings.

14) Some of the ladies' hats at the Ascot races make them look _____ .

15) The wealthy family live in a _____ neighbourhood.

16) He is feverish, with a high _____ and a headache.

17) "Her family has farmed for five generations: _____ is in her blood!"

18) It is planned to complete the new sewage _____ plant next year.

19) Students filled the _____ theatre to hear the eminent speaker.

20) _____ reports from the area indicate a worsening situation.

Score [/ 10]

Across

216

1. The application of medical care to cure disease, heal injuries, or ease symptoms.
3. Having a feeling of dread or apprehension.
5. Used to describe a climate that has a range of temperatures within moderate limits.
7. Having happened or appeared not long ago.
8. A small decorative object displayed for its beauty.
9. Completely unreasonable and not at all sensible or acceptable.
12. Feeling bitter and unhappy because of another's advantages, possessions, or luck.
13. The adverb of 'recent'.
15. An educational speech on a particular subject made before an audience.
16. An object used to produce musical notes.

Across (continued)

18. Extremely large, powerful, or great.
19. A small hole or wound made by a sharp object.

Down

1. The degree of heat as an inherent quality of objects.
2. Successful and flourishing, especially earning or producing great wealth.
4. Practical, usually comfortable and hard-wearing, and not worn as an adornment.
6. The occupation or business of cultivating land, producing crops and raising livestock.
10. A naturally occurring opening in the surface of the Earth's crust through which molten, gaseous, and solid material is ejected.
11. Large and projecting.
14. A piece of upholstered furniture on which two or more people can sit side by side.
17. A way, path, or road for travelling from one place to another.

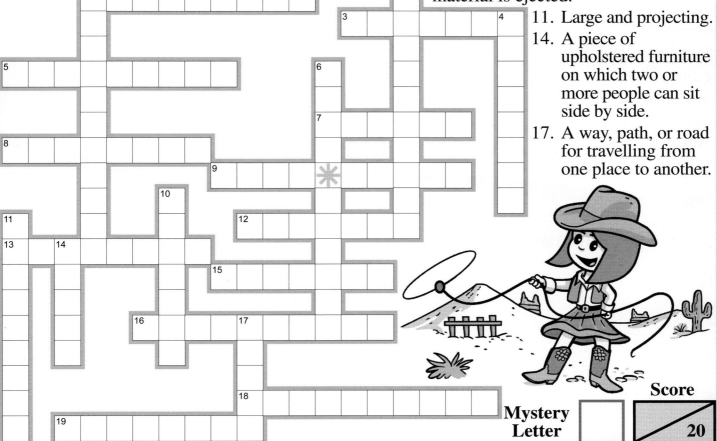

Mystery Letter

Score

20

25

Dickens's
Page of Knowledge
Pioneers and Achievements

Sir Francis Chichester ⑦
Clue: Born in 1901, this master mariner made history in 1967. His historic voyage took nine months and one day. He received a hero's welcome on his return to Plymouth and was knighted.

Robert Edwin Peary ⑤
Clue: After a journey on foot of over 1,300 miles, over rugged terrain and in a hostile environment, this American pioneer reached his objective on 6th April, 1909.

The Pilgrim Fathers ②
Clue: 102 Quaker men and women left Plymouth aboard the 'Mayflower'. They arrived at their destination on 6th September, 1620 and named it after their port of departure.

Yuri Gagarin ⑩
Clue: This Soviet ex-fighter pilot made history in April 1961, when television screens around the world showed him in his capsule. Returning safely, he was lauded in Moscow.

Sir Edmond Hillary ③
Clue: Born in New Zealand, this man ascended to fame aided by Sherpa Tensing. He succeeded in reaching the pinnacle of his achievement at 29,000 feet on 29th May, 1953.

Pioneer	Achievement
1. _____ /	_____
2. _____ /	_____
3. _____ /	_____
4. _____ /	_____
5. _____ /	_____

North Pole · Manned Flight
Settle America · South Pole
Single-handed around the World
Cross Channel Flight
Orbit the Earth · Climb Everest
Moon Walk · Swim the Channel

"Link the name of the pioneer with the achievement for which they are famous."

Neil Armstrong ❹
Clue: "One small step for man, one giant leap for mankind." The words he spoke as he stepped onto a dusty and rocky surface. For millions of years and from 250,000 miles away, mankind dreamed of this achievement.

Orville and Wilbur Wright ❶
Clue: These two brothers from Ohio were bicycle manufacturers. They made history on 17th December, 1903 travelling only 39 metres at Kittyhawk.

Louis Blériot ❽
Clue: It took 31 minutes to travel less than 25 miles, but this journey had never been made before. This Frenchman succeeded on 25th July, 1909 to do what millions of travellers now take for granted.

Captain Matthew Webb ❻
Clue: On 25th August, 1875, he became the first person to complete this journey without the use of artificial aids. He travelled over 39 miles in 21 hours and 5 minutes.

Roald Amundsen ❾
Clue: He was born in 1872 in Oslo. On 16th December, 1911 he reached his destination, beating Englishman Robert Falcon Scott by only 35 days.

Pioneer   Achievement

6. _____ / _____

7. _____ / _____

8. _____ / _____

9. _____ / _____

10. _____ / _____

responsible	visible	invisible
rifle	ignorant	ignorance
abundance	attendance	appearance
ceiling	perceive	deceit

Exercise 217a

1) Nelson raised the _____ to his blind eye and said, "I see no ships!"

2) The burglar's main objective was to _____ through the cupboards and drawers.

3) The _____ on wage rises meant a maximum increase of three percent.

4) They are an extremely poor family living in _____ conditions.

5) In Hinduism, the cow is considered _____ and symbolic of abundance.

6) "Look at this mess! Whoever is _____ had better clean it up!"

7) The Wicked _____ of the East ruled Munchkin Country in *The Wizard of Oz.*

8) Lemon juice can be used as an _____ ink that appears when heated.

9) The _____ at the rock concert was in excess of 30,000 fans.

10) She is a _____ person and is often accused of lying.

Score ⬛ 10

Exercise 217b

11) The two nations show great animosity and _____ towards each other.

12) Given the publicity surrounding the case, his _____ was unbelievable.

13) The barbecue was a great success with an _____ of food and drink.

14) The aircraft descended below the clouds and the runway became _____ .

15) She could not stay long but she felt obliged to put in an _____ .

16) "I know you'll disagree but I'm sure I can _____ just a hint of ginger."

17) The fabric tends to _____ easily and makes the jacket look shabby.

18) Military tacticians use the art of decoy and _____ to confuse an enemy.

19) The _____ 's magnitude measured 7.8 on the Richter scale.

20) They were _____ of the danger until it was too late.

Score ⬛ 10

deceitful
hatred
witch
wrinkle

earthquake
sacred
wretched
telescope

**Word Bank
TOTAL
4,340**

Across

2. Feeling very unhappy or ill.
6. A violent shaking of the Earth's crust.
9. A line or crease between small folds of skin that forms on the face as a result of ageing.
11. Lack of knowledge, awareness, education, or enlightenment.
14. Accountable to somebody for an action or for the successful carrying out of a duty.
16. To notice something, especially something that escapes the notice of others.
17. Dedicated to a deity or religious purpose.
18. The act of emerging, arriving, or coming into existence.

Down

1. Hidden from view.
3. A feeling of intense dislike, anger, hostility, or animosity.
4. Intentionally misleading or fraudulent in lying to people, or not telling them the whole truth.
5. The overhead surface of a room.
7. A more than plentiful quantity of something.
8. An instance of being at an event.
9. Somebody, especially a woman, who is supposed to have magical powers that are most often used malevolently.
10. Capable of being seen by, or perceptible to, the human eye.
12. Lacking knowledge and education in general or in a specific subject.
13. A device for making distant objects appear nearer and larger.
14. A gun with a long barrel that is fired from the shoulder.
15. The act or practice of deceiving or misleading somebody.

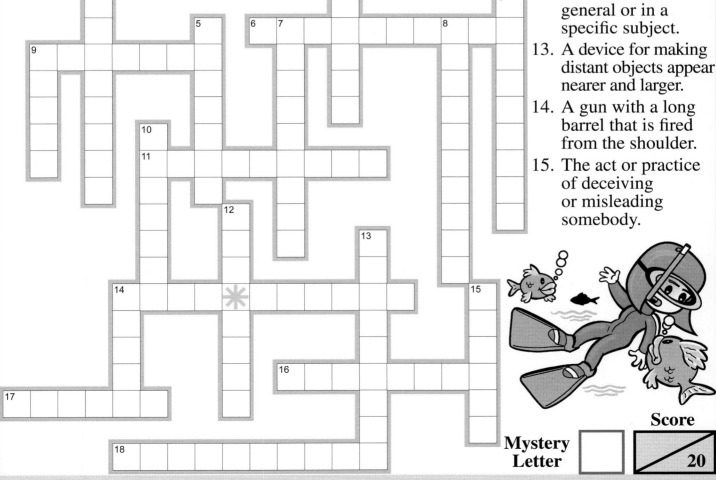

Mystery Letter

Score

20

Across

218

4. Somebody in a bank who deals directly with customers and handles routine account transactions.
6. A set of moving steps attached to a continuously circulating belt.
9. A device used to carry out arithmetical operations.
10. An agreement to get married.
13. A warm, thick, waterproof, hip-length jacket with a hood.
15. Riding breeches that are wide at the hip and narrow round the calves.
17. The exchanging of goods or services in return for other goods or services.

Across (continued)

18. To persistently annoy, attack, or bother somebody.
19. Somebody who works in, or is in charge of, a library.
20. The largest and lowest-pitched instrument of the violin family.

Down

1. A woman legal inheritor of the property, position, or title of another when that person dies.
2. A triangular-shaped, stringed instrument.
3. Not allowing oil or grease to soak into it or pass through it.
5. Showing an aggressive lack of respect in speech or behaviour.
7. A weapon consisting of a bow attached crosswise to a stock with a cranking mechanism and a trigger.
8. Cosmetic products especially for the face, for example lipstick and mascara.
11. A plant that has clusters of fragrant bluish-purple flowers that produce a fragrant oil.
12. An enclosure or large cage where birds are kept.
14. The currency unit of most of the countries in the European Union.
16. Parallel to the horizon.

Score

Mystery Letter [ ] [/ 20]

engagement   harp
heiress   bartering
aviary   crossbow
horizontal   makeup

Word Bank
TOTAL
4,360

Exercise 218a

1) He often played bass guitar but used the _____ in the jazz trio.

2) They changed their sterling into _____ before going on holiday to Portugal.

3) "Disbelief in her own ability is a basic part of her _____ ."

4) His agent secured the entertainer a week-long _____ in Las Vegas.

5) She wore a tweed jacket, _____ and riding boots.

6) _____ is common among people with no access to a cash economy.

7) The stories of William Tell and his skill with the _____ are legendary.

8) The butcher wrapped the sausages in _____ paper.

9) As _____ , she would become wealthy after her millionaire father's death.

10) The _____ helped him locate the book he needed.   **Score** / 10

Exercise 218b

11) "Don't _____ on about your team's problems, we're tired of hearing about them!"

12) The _____ was invented by the Inuit to wear when hunting and kayaking.

13) The _____ was out of order so they used the stairs instead.

14) Use of a _____ in mathematics lessons is restricted by some schools.

15) He shows skill and strength in the gymnastics _____ bar event.

16) The court marshall's verdict was to _____ the soldier for misconduct.

17) He continued to _____ his father until he agreed to buy him a new bicycle.

18) _____ water is perhaps the oldest known method of wearing fragrance.

19) She has an _____ in the garden in which she breeds budgerigars.

20) "Watch your tongue, young man, and don't be so _____!" **Score** / 10

comedy	embroidery	bawl
excise	marigold	fidget
uncomfortable	pyjamas	decisions
blowpipe	crypt	nursing

Exercise 219a

1) Twenty one degrees Celsius converts to 69.8 degrees _____ .

2) Her aged mother required constant care and was moved into a _____ home.

3) The disgruntled fans continued to _____ abusively at the referee.

4) The police wanted to _____ the body for further forensic examination.

5) His account was embellished with a rich _____ of fictitious details.

6) He had a shower and put on his _____ and dressing gown.

7) She has been _____ since being made redundant six months ago.

8) The adverse comments had _____ the doubt in his mind: he might fail.

9) *The _____ of Errors* is Shakespeare's shortest play, and one of his most farcical.

10) "Don't _____ with your pen while I'm talking to you!"   **Score** [/10]

Exercise 219b

11) He raised the _____ to his lips and fired the poisoned dart at the animal.

12) They boarded the _____ for the short flight across the Solent.

13) The _____ , native to tropical America, is a common garden plant.

14) The surgeon used a scalpel to _____ the cyst from below the skin.

15) The court found him guilty, _____ him £200, and ordered him to pay costs.

16) It was a long journey and the hard wooden seats were _____ .

17) The architect took _____ and drew a plan of the house.

18) They kissed under the sprig of _____ hanging over the doorway.

19) Many valuable religious artefacts were found stored in the _____ .

20) "You must compromise and make some tough _____ ."   **Score** [/10]

sown
mistletoe
exhume
Fahrenheit

unemployed
fined
hovercraft
measurements

Word Bank TOTAL 4,380

Across

219

1. The craft of using needlework to make decorative designs.
5. To shout something in a loud and usually aggressive voice.
6. To dig up a corpse from a grave.
9. An evergreen parasitic shrub that grows on trees such as apple or oak.
10. The sizes, lengths, quantities, or rates of things that have been measured.
13. Entertainment that is amusing.
14. Punished by the taking of a fixed amount of money from somebody who has broken a rule or a law.
15. An underground room or vault, often below a church.
17. Not used, or jobless.
19. To move about in a restless, absent-minded, or uneasy manner.
20. Things that somebody chooses or makes up his or her mind about, after considering them and other possible choices.

Down

2. A long, narrow tube through which darts or pellets are shot by blowing.
3. A temperature scale where water freezes at 32° and boils at 212°.
4. Tax imposed on goods for a domestic market only.
7. A vehicle that can travel over land and water supported by a cushion of air.

Down (continued)

8. Feeling a lack of, or not providing, physical comfort.
11. Scattered or planted.
12. A common garden plant with scented stems and strikingly rich yellow or orange flowers.
16. A light loose pair of trousers and a matching loose-fitting shirt for wearing in bed.
18. The profession or task of looking after people who are ill or injured.

Mystery Letter

Score /20

benevolent	pyramid	influenza
mosque	rapped	supersonic
upholstery	vehicles	fiction
boutique	fiord	indoors

Exercise 220a

1) The _____ checked his watch and then blew his whistle to end the game.

2) The _____ was carved out of the mountains by glacial erosion.

3) It is a huge, _____ house: many extra rooms have been added over the years.

4) The muezzin leads the call to Salat from the _____ 's minaret.

5) Many Victorian businessmen were _____ and provided for their workers.

6) The banquette had seen better days and the _____ needed replacing.

7) A wadi is a dry water coarse but in North Africa it is also called an _____ .

8) "It's too wet outside, you'll have to play _____ today."

9) The *Harry Potter* stories are great works of _____ by J.K. Rowling.

10) The hunters tracked the animal by following its _____ .

Score [/10]

Exercise 220b

11) The _____ time was verified later as a new Olympic record.

12) The policeman tried the handle, then he _____ on the door with his truncheon.

13) It is an _____ contest because her opponent is injured.

14) It took over 2,300,000 giant stone blocks to make the Cheops _____ .

15) She owns a small _____ in the high street that sells fashionable clothes.

16) *Concorde* was the only successful _____ passenger aircraft.

17) The weather _____ on top of the church steeple indicates an easterly wind.

18) Astronomers formerly used a _____ to measure the angles of stars.

19) A queue of stationary _____ blocked the motorway.

20) _____ can be fatal, particularly among the old and infirm.

Score [/10]

Across

220

3. Continuing for too long and with many changes of subject.
6. Conveyances, usually wheeled, used on land for carrying people or goods.
7. A solid shape with sloping triangular sides.
9. Not authorized by the proper, official or other authority.
12. Not measurably the same.
13. The stuffing, cushions, fabric, and other materials used to upholster chairs and couches.
15. A long, narrow coastal inlet with steep sides often formed by glacial action.

Across (continued)

17. A 90° arc representing one fourth of the circumference of a circle.
18. The visible trail of an animal.
20. Fertile ground in a desert where the level of underground water rises to or near ground level.

Down

1. A small shop that sells fashionable goods.
2. A flat blade, mounted as part of a set in a circle so as to rotate under the action of wind or liquid.
4. Showing kindness and goodwill.
5. Struck something with a quick, sharp blow.
8. A viral illness producing a high temperature, sore throat, runny nose, headache, dry cough and muscle pain.
10. Novels and stories that describe imaginary people and events.
11. Capable of exceeding the speed at which sound travels through the air.
14. Into or inside a building.
16. A building in which Muslims worship.
19. An official who oversees the play in a sport or game.

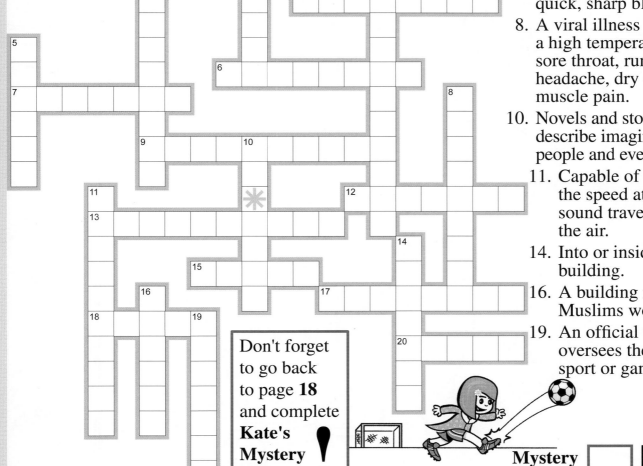

Don't forget to go back to page **18** and complete **Kate's Mystery Word.** ! ●

Mystery Letter

Score 20

At the Fishmonger's

Can you find all these words in the picture below? Write the correct word against each number.

wrapper	fins	oysters	crabs	tongs
counter	galoshes	apron	cash register	boater
ice	skeleton	jar	lobster	scales

1._____ 2._____ 3._____

4._____ 5._____ 6._____

7._____ 8._____ 9._____

10._____ 11._____ 12._____

13._____ 14._____ 15._____

At the Recreation Park

Can you find all these words in the picture below? Write the correct word against each number. When you have finished you can colour in the picture if you want to.

acrobat	tier	decal	hood	ramp
goalpost	football	runner	Rollerblades	tennis
skateboard	cyclist	scooter	jogger	rugby ball

1._____ 2._____ 3._____

4._____ 5._____ 6._____

7._____ 8._____ 9._____

10._____ 11._____ 12._____

13._____ 14._____ 15._____

© 2006 Stephen Curran

Across

221

3. Salt, pepper, or any herb or spice used to give additional flavour to food.
4. Damaging somebody's dignity or pride.
5. A sleeveless dress.
8. A metal wind instrument with keys and a reed that comes in several sizes and registers.
11. A deceptive move in a competitive sport.
12. The scientific study of animals.
13. A sword with a long, slender blade.
17. A severe tropical storm.
18. Somebody who votes or speaks on behalf of others.
19. Circular brass percussion instruments.
20. Somebody who is in extreme poverty.

Down

1. The ability to endure waiting or delay.
2. Difficult or impossible to understand.
6. A technician involved in the taking of X-rays or in radiotherapy.
7. Conventionally believed to be appropriate for a woman or girl.
9. A building that contains, or formerly contained, hop-drying kilns.
10. A mixture of egg whites and sugar beaten until stiff, then cooked.
14. An electrical appliance that keeps items cool through artificial means.
15. A country dance in which four couples form a square.
16. A four-sided plane figure in which each angle is a right angle.

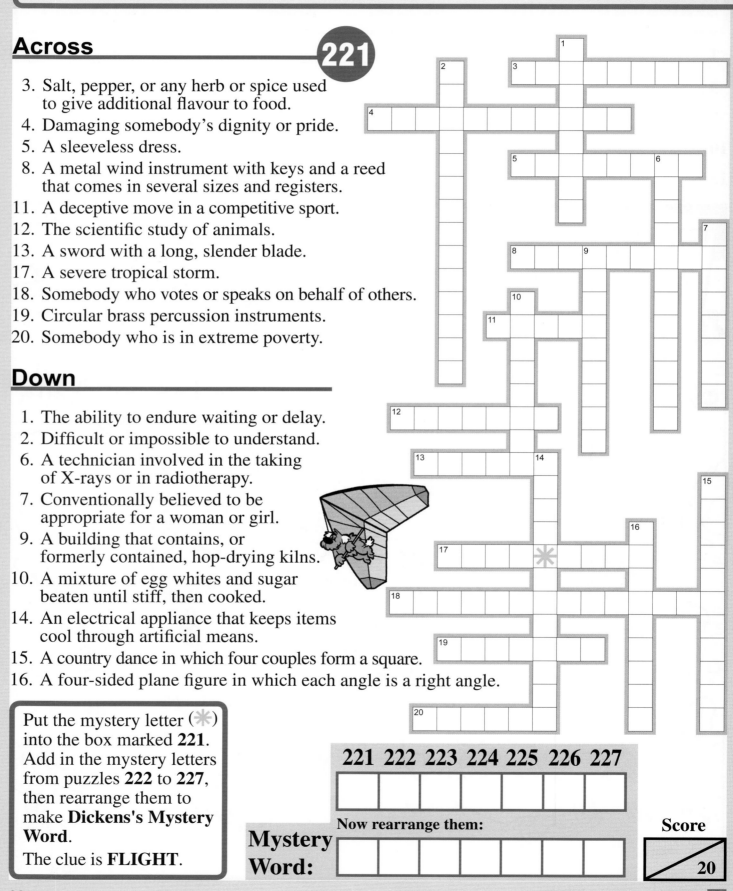

Put the mystery letter (✳) into the box marked **221**. Add in the mystery letters from puzzles **222** to **227**, then rearrange them to make **Dickens's Mystery Word**.
The clue is **FLIGHT**.

221	222	223	224	225	226	227

Mystery Word:

Now rearrange them:

Score

/20

patience
oast-house
square-dance
pauper

rapier
radiographer
representative
seasoning

Exercise 221a

1) They bought an old Kent _____ to convert into a home.

2) *The Prince and the* _____ was written by Mark Twain in 1881.

3) The instructions had been badly translated and were _____ .

4) Many languages use the masculine and _____ definite article with nouns.

5) Her poor examination results were not _____ of her ability.

6) It can be _____ to be asked to stand in front of the class and sing.

7) The moisture in timber is reduced by the process of _____ .

8) The _____ examined the X-ray that she had taken and processed.

9) Both the clarinet and the _____ are reed instruments.

10) His favourite dessert is lemon _____ pie.

Score / **10**

Exercise 221b

11) He was the caller at the _____ and knew all the moves.

12) Food was kept in a cool pantry before the invention of the _____ .

13) "You are really trying my _____ : I'm trying hard not to lose my temper."

14) He parried a thrust from his fencing opponent's _____ .

15) A rugby pitch is a large _____ , about 100 metres long by 70 metres wide.

16) The percussionist brought the two _____ together with a loud crash.

17) With a deceptive _____ he jinked first left, then right, straight through the defence.

18) Her school uniform consists of a white blouse under a navy _____ dress.

19) The continent of Australia provides _____ with many unique animals.

20) He refilled the _____ lamp with paraffin and lit it.

Score / **10**

toga   **segment**   **plane**
unsympathetic   **recapitulate**   **glimmer**
persist   **mammoth**   **actual**
eruption   **overtake**   **solution**

Across

(222)

1. Real and existing as fact.
4. A word indicating the only person or thing that does not apply to a statement just made, or a fact that modifies the truth of that statement.
6. A hand tool for smoothing or shaping wood.
7. A large, extinct elephant that had long curved tusks and was covered with hair.
11. To draw level with and pass a person or vehicle travelling in the same direction.
13. A celestial body that is composed of a mass of ice and dust and has a long, luminous tail.
15. A plant of the cabbage family with green, purple or white lower heads that are cooked and eaten as a vegetable.
16. Relating to, located at, or found in the regions surrounding the North or South Poles.
18. To go over the main points of something again.
19. The violent ejection of material, such as gas, steam, ash, or lava, from a volcano.

Down

2. Something that helps to solve a mystery or crime.
3. Showing no sympathy or approval.
5. Any one of the parts or sections into which an object or group is divided.
8. A method of successfully dealing with a problem or difficulty.

Down (continued)

9. Causing intense excitement.
10. To emit a faint or intermittent light.
12. An outer garment worn by the citizens of Ancient Rome.
14. A game in which two teams of 11 players try to kick or head a round ball into the goal defended by the opposing team.
16. To continue steadily or obstinately despite problems, difficulties or obstacles.
17. A long, stiff piece of rope or cord with a sliding noose at one end, used especially for catching horses and cattle.

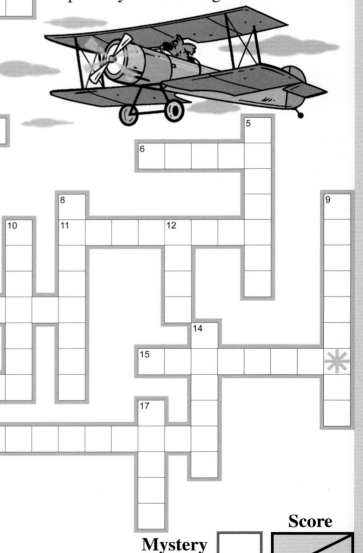

Mystery Letter

Score

20

lasso	**clue**	**Word Bank**
polar	**broccoli**	**TOTAL**
soccer	**comet**	**4,440**
thrilling	**except**	

Exercise 222a

1) He spread the adhesive _____ on the inner tube and applied the patch.

2) The secretary asked the chairman to _____ the main points.

3) Many scientists believe that the _____ caps are shrinking due to global warming.

4) The _____ was a Roman garment worn exclusively by men: women wore the stola.

5) The _____ sped across the night sky, exhibiting a coma and trailing a tail in its wake.

6) Over 240 million people in more than 200 countries regularly play _____ .

7) It was a _____ task to distribute aid to the victims of the tsunami.

8) " _____ looks like green cauliflower," observed her young son.

9) She peeled an orange and gave a _____ to each of her children.

10) The cowboy in the rodeo used a lariat to _____ steers.   **Score** [/ 10]

Exercise 222b

11) An allergic reaction caused an angry _____ over his entire body.

12) It was a _____ race with the world's best sprinters vying for first place.

13) Everyone came to the wedding _____ his aunt who was taken ill suddenly.

14) He had to _____ the bottom of the door to allow it to clear the new carpet.

15) He managed to _____ the slow-moving lorry when the road widened.

16) "There's a _____ of hope that they are still alive but time is running out."

17) He was _____ about their plight and ignored requests for help.

18) They were on board HMS *Victory*, standing on the _____ spot where Nelson died.

19) The forecast is that the rain will _____ until the end of the week.

20) "He's hopeless! He hasn't a _____ what's going on."   **Score** [/ 10]

annually	raccoon	bouquet
excavator	overweight	adore
missing	commando	radiant
thrifty	compact	mixture

Exercise 223a

1) The daring _____ night raid took the enemy completely by surprise.

2) The teacher asked the class to _____ themselves into groups of six.

3) He hung the _____ between two palm trees and climbed in.

4) The sailor took the _____ and leaned over the gunwales to scrub the ship's bottom.

5) The doctor told him that he was _____ and should take more exercise.

6) She believes that her _____ is preordained and that she cannot affect the outcome.

7) The wine has a full, rich _____ and a robust taste.

8) A large mechanical _____ was digging a trench across the field.

9) The interest on her savings account is paid _____ .

10) "Take some cough _____ to soothe your throat."

Score [10]

Exercise 223b

11) She opened her _____ and checked in the mirror how she looked.

12) He derived great satisfaction from _____ the crossword puzzle.

13) They are a very happy couple: it is obvious that they _____ each other.

14) He was always _____ the bus and arriving late for school.

15) "Your report is too vague: it lacks _____ and a definitive conclusion."

16) Her parents taught her to be _____ and to save some of her pocket money.

17) "He is such a _____ : he has nothing interesting to say and never plays games."

18) The _____ is nocturnal, omnivorous and often considered a pest.

19) The marathon runners _____ and dehydrated in the heat.

20) She looked happy and _____ on her wedding day.

Score [10]

ae

bore
completing
structure
perspired

hammock
fate
organise
hog

Across 223

5. A large mechanical digger.
7. A bunch of cut flowers that have been specially chosen or arranged.
11. To love somebody intensely.
14. To have secreted fluid from the sweat glands through the pores of the skin.
15. A small mammal that has greyish-black fur, black patches around the eyes, and a long bushy ringed tail.
18. With more weight than is considered healthy for somebody of a specific height, build, or age.
19. Every year or once a year.
20. To become, or make something, more dense or firmly packed.

Down

1. A substance containing several ingredients combined or blended together.
2. To make a deep hole in something.
3. A hanging bed of canvas or netting suspended at both ends by ropes tied between two supports.
4. The way in which different parts of something link or work together.
6. Finishing something.
8. Not present in an expected place, absent, or lost.
9. A force or principle believed to predetermine events.

Down (continued)

10. To oversee the coordination of the various elements of something.
12. Lit with a bright or glowing light.
13. Managing money and resources in a cautious and sensible way so as to waste as little as possible.
16. A member of a military force specially trained to make dangerous raids.
17. A full-grown domestic pig.

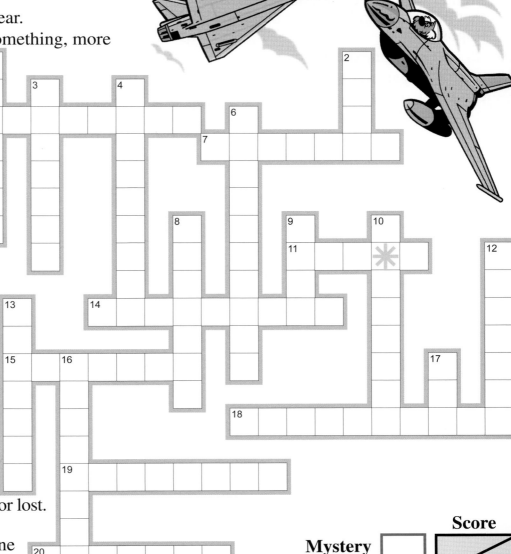

Mystery Letter

Score / 20

appendix   **combining**   **premature**
tension   **antler**   **germ**
curiously   **memorial**   **shy**
misconceive   **expenditure**   **bibliography**

Across

224

3. Joining or mixing together.
6. A solid, bony, branched horn found in pairs on the heads of animals, especially males, of the deer family.
10. An amount of money spent.
12. A list of books and articles consulted, appearing at the end of a book.
13. A narrow crack or opening.
16. Occurring, existing, or developing earlier than is expected, normal, or advisable.
17. Mental worry or emotional strain that makes natural, relaxed behaviour impossible.
19. Strangely or unexpectedly.
20. A microorganism, especially one that can cause disease.

Down

1. Not clearly belonging to one or other of two categories.
2. Something different from, and able to serve as a substitute for, something else.
4. Increases by a considerable number, amount, or degree.
5. Cooks something in fat over high heat.
7. To grasp the meaning or nature of something.
8. Something that is intended to remind people of a person who has died, or an event in which people died.
9. Dying from lack of air.
11. To fail to understand something correctly.
14. A collection of separate material at the end of a book or document.
15. The feel and appearance of a surface, especially how rough or smooth it is.
18. Reserved, diffident, and uncomfortable in the company of others.

Mystery Letter

Score 20

alternative   **comprehend**
texture   **suffocating**
crevice   **fries**
borderline   **multiplies**

Word Bank
TOTAL
4,480

Exercise 224a

1) He had the _____ of an idea and developed it into a lucrative invention.

2) The windows were sealed and the heat in the room was _____ .

3) Her score was _____ but she just scraped through into the final.

4) The mechanic adjusted the pulley to increase the belt's _____ .

5) The longest _____ ever removed measured 23.5cm (9.2in) in length.

6) Her doctor accepts that _____ medicines may be beneficial.

7) Rabbits are extremely prolific: one pair _____ to millions in a few years.

8) She appeared to _____ his offer of help as interference.

9) The climber hammered a piton into a _____ in the rock.

10) The author's _____ listed seventeen novels. **Score** ⟋ 10

Exercise 224b

11) The Menin Gate in Ypres is an impressive _____ to those missing in battle.

12) The company could save on a member of staff by _____ the two jobs.

13) "Don't be _____ ! Come in and meet some of the other children."

14) They found an _____ recently shed by a deer.

15) "It would be _____ to name the suspect with insufficient evidence."

16) The decorator stippled the wall to give it a rough, grainy _____ .

17) "My gran always _____ sausages but I prefer them grilled."

18) The business is profitable, with income significantly exceeding _____ .

19) He finds it difficult to _____ fully the scale of the task.

20) The baby looked around _____ at her strange new world. **Score** ⟋ 10

thoughtfully	suffocate	admires
eventual	memorise	permanently
coping	supplying	amuses
completed	miaow	signature

Exercise 225a

1) Her cat would stand at the back door and _____ loudly to attract attention.

2) Although it is a team event, extra points are awarded for _____ effort.

3) Her mother seemed to be _____ well on her own after her stay in hospital.

4) "Kim's game" tests a person's ability to observe and _____ specific details.

5) Bad weather will prevent the building work from being _____ on time.

6) He used indelible ink to mark _____ every piece of his games kit.

7) Violet Szabo was a _____ who was awarded the George Cross posthumously.

8) It is a relaxing place with a _____ and solitude all of its own.

9) The copse and the three fields _____ the farmer's entire estate.

20) He stood his ground _____ as the enemy approached.   **Score** ⟋ 10

Exercise 225b

11) It is easy to be overly strict and to _____ a person's self-expression.

12) He paced up and down _____ , frustrated by the delay.

13) The report was written _____ to avoid causing the family distress.

14) He thanked the company for _____ valuable equipment to the aid agency.

15) *The Liberty Bell* by Sousa was used as the programme's _____ tune.

16) He listened to the salesman's _____ but decided against buying the car.

17) "Everyone _____ a person who strives to overcome adversity."

18) The _____ winner came from the leading group of cyclists.

19) "I _____ last night's episode: you can borrow it if you like."

20) "He _____ me with his jokes and witty remarks."   **Score** ⟋ 10

Word Bank TOTAL 4,500

Across

225

3. Quietness, calmness and tranquillity.
5. A separate entity or thing.
6. In a manner that showed annoyance by being kept waiting or by being delayed.
7. In a considerately and kindly way.
10. Carried out or accomplished something.
11. Has a high opinion of somebody or something.
13. The characteristic cry made by a domestic cat.
14. Somebody's name signed by him or her.
15. A remarkably brave woman.
16. To move or run with short, quick, light steps.

Across (continued)

17. Giving, selling, or making available something that is wanted or needed.
18. Lasting for ever or for a very long time, especially without undergoing significant change.

Down

1. In a deliberately and openly disobedient manner.
2. To deprive somebody of air or prevent somebody from breathing, or to be unable to breathe.
4. Dealing successfully with a difficult problem or situation.
8. Secured, fastened, or strengthened something using tape.
9. To be made up of something.
11. Making somebody smile or laugh, or think that something is funny.
12. Happening in the course of time or events, usually much later.
13. To commit something to memory.

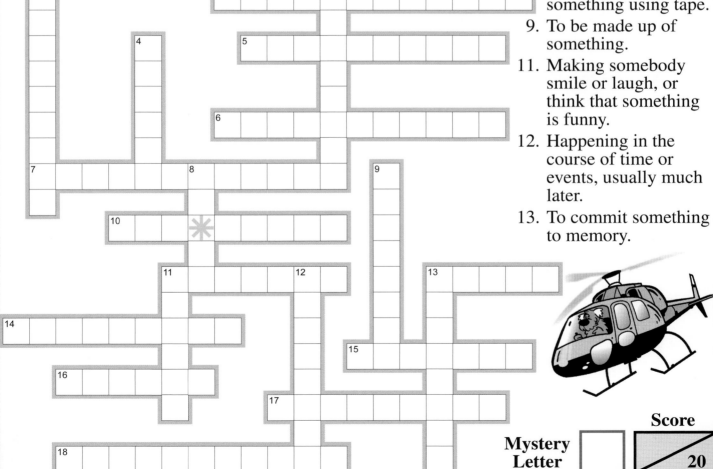

Mystery Letter

Score
20

amaze   suffocated   conscientiously
excites   habitual   posture
defuses   highlight   stallion
allocating   cope   moo

Across

226

3. Setting something aside for a particular purpose.
4. An adult male horse, especially one kept for breeding.
6. Makes a bomb or mine harmless by removing its detonating device.
9. To fill somebody with wonder, astonishment, or extreme surprise.
12. Performing a task in a thorough and diligent manner.
15. Carried out or revealed in the expectation that anything done or revealed will be kept private.
16. The most memorable, important, or exciting part of an experience or event.

Across (continued)

17. Kept somebody occupied or entertained by providing entertainment or an interesting task.
18. A smaller-than-usual version of something.

Down

1. Done regularly and frequently.
2. To steal things.
4. Confined or restricted somebody or something with adverse effects.
5. Makes a person or animal feel nervous apprehension.
7. Not flowing or moving.
8. In a manner that demonstrates a willingness to obey.
10. To produce the deep drawn-out sound that a cow makes.
11. A frame of mind or attitude to a particular subject.
12. Misunderstanding of a situation or the facts.
13. To deal successfully with a difficult problem or situation.
14. Somebody who is extremely wicked or cruel.

Mystery Letter

Score

20

© 2006 Stephen Curran

thieve	miniature	Word Bank
obediently	stagnant	TOTAL
confidential	amused	4,520
fiend	confusion	

Exercise 226a

1) The victims were buried under the avalanche and were _____ .

2) He is a _____ for railway history and devotes all his spare time to research.

3) It is understandable that desperate, hungry people are driven to _____ food.

4) "She is an _____ liar whose word cannot be trusted!"

5) The information is extremely sensitive and must remain _____ .

6) The report cites many examples of abuse to _____ the regime's brutality.

7) The situation was chaotic and they became separated in the _____ .

8) His calm and quiet manner _____ any tense situations and averts crises.

9) He is a magnificent _____ , measuring over 16 hands high.

20) He wondered how he would _____ in an emergency.

Score 10

Exercise 226b

11) His dog was well-trained and responded to his instructions _____ .

12) Her natural talent and ability never failed to _____ her instructor.

13) The sales figures have been _____ for too long and need to improve.

14) "Keep your baby sister _____ while I'm busy in the kitchen."

15) He is tall, has poor _____ and, in later life, will become round-shouldered.

16) He avoided any argument by _____ an equal share to each of them.

17) She can be relied upon to apply herself _____ to any task.

18) The _____ railway is one tenth scale and runs on a narrow gauge track.

19) He has become lethargic and nothing _____ him any more.

20) A cow's deep _____ broke the early morning stillness.

Score 10

exorbitant	congeal	coped
justification	exchequer	apostrophe
bistro	simile	nutritious
temporary	Celsius	duvet

Exercise 227a

1) The thermal resistance of a _____ is indicated by a Tog value.

2) They believed that opposition to their plan would _____ if they delayed.

3) They arranged to meet at the _____ for a sandwich and a cup of coffee.

4) He turned the spanner _____ to loosen the nut.

5) _____ fever causes many instances of damaged heart valves.

6) The Chancellor of the _____ put his budget speech into his red briefcase.

7) The word *fo'c's'le* demonstrates use of the _____ .

8) The workmen finished the road repairs and removed the _____ sign.

9) Investigators needed _____ evidence to prove who wrote the letter.

20) They _____ without him but it was not easy.

Score / 10

Exercise 227b

11) India gained _____ from Britain in 1947.

12) A degree _____ (°C) is a unit of temperature named after a Swedish astronomer.

13) She is _____ to having her own way and to never being opposed.

14) House prices in the city are _____ and unaffordable for most people.

15) *'Right as rain'* and *'black as coal'* are just two examples of a _____ .

16) He is an _____ person who prefers his own company to that of others.

17) An ancient Greek _____ had tiers of seats on both sides and at one end.

18) The rolls of _____ once used in cameras have been replaced by digital technology.

19) She was upset but that was no _____ for her rudeness.

20) A diet of _____ food is essential for good health.

Score / 10

Across

227

2. A factual film or TV programme.
4. Using or measured on an international metric temperature scale on which water freezes at 0° and boils at 100°.
6. The government department responsible for collecting taxes and managing public spending.
8. Annoying, inconsiderate, or indifferent to the comfort or needs of neighbours.
10. A small restaurant or bar.
13. A person suffering any painful condition of the joints or muscles that is not caused by infection or injury.
14. Freedom from dependence on, or control by, another person, organization, or state.

Across (continued)

15. A thin coating of a substance covering the surface of something.
16. To become thick and solid or cause a liquid to thicken and solidify.
17. The punctuation mark used to show where letters are omitted and to mark the possessive.
18. Used to, or familiar with, something or somebody.
19. Lasting for, or relating to, a limited time.

Down

1. Past participle of *'cope'*.
2. A bed quilt made up of broad channels stuffed with down or synthetic material.
3. Something that justifies an action or attitude.
5. A figure of speech that draws a comparison between two different things.
7. In the opposite direction to the way the hands of a clock move.
9. Containing minerals, vitamins, and other substances that promote health.
11. Far greater or higher than is reasonable.
12. A large, enclosed, flat area surrounded by tiers of seats for spectators.

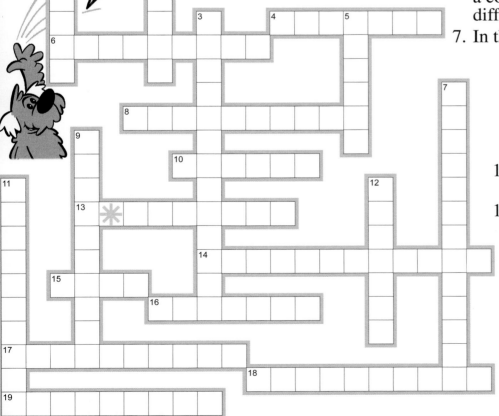

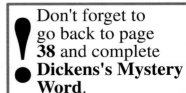

Don't forget to go back to page **38** and complete **Dickens's Mystery Word**.

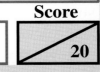

Mystery Letter

Score

20

51

Book Ten Word List

abrupt
abundance
abundant
accurate
accuse
accustom
accustomed
acre
actual
addition
admires
admission
adore
agriculture
allocating
alternative
amaze
amused
amuses
announce
annual
annually
anorak
anticlockwise
antisocial
antler
anxious
apostrophe
appeal
appearance
appendix
arouse
attendance
August
author
autumn
average
aviary
avoid
baggage
bartering
bawl
benevolent
bibliography

bicycle
biscuit
bistro
blowpipe
borderline
bore
bouquet
boutique
brief
broccoli
business
calculator
camera
candidate
career
carriage
cashier
ceiling
Celsius
cement
certificate
choice
clue
cocoa
coil
colony
combining
comedy
comet
commando
compact
completed
completing
comprehend
comprise
conclude
condemn
conductor
conferred
confident
confidential
confusion
congeal
conscientiously

consent
contempt
continent
contract
control
convince
cope
coped
coping
couch
cough
crevice
criminal
crooked
crossbow
crypt
curious
curiously
cushion
cymbals
debate
debt
deceit
deceitful
decisions
declare
decline
decrease
defence
defiantly
defuses
delicate
deny
depth
determination
determine
discourage
documentary
double-bass
doubt
duvet
earthquake
elephant
embrace

embroidery
engagement
engineer
enterprise
entirely
eruption
escalator
Euro
eventual
excavator
except
exchequer
excise
excites
exhume
exorbitant
expenditure
expense
expensive
experiment
Fahrenheit
fate
fault
feint
feminine
festival
fiction
fidget
fiend
fierce
film
fined
fiord
foolish
force
forehead
fragment
fries
fund
furnace
fury
garage
general
generally

Book Ten Word List

geography	invisible	New Zealand	prominent
germ	jealous	ninety	proportion
ghost	jodhpurs	nursing	prosperous
glimmer	juice	nutritious	protection
glorious	justification	oasis	puncture
governor	keen	oast-house	pyjamas
grateful	lasso	obediently	pyramid
greaseproof	laundry	o'clock	quadrant
Greece	lavender	organise	raccoon
greet	lecture	ornament	radiant
grudge	length	orphan	radiographer
habitual	liberal	ounce	rambling
hammock	librarian	overtake	rapier
harass	lodging	overweight	rapped
harp	loose	palm	recapitulate
hatred	lungs	patience	recent
heaviness	machine	patter	recently
heiress	major	pauper	rectangle
heroine	majority	pause	referee
hesitate	makeup	peace	refrigerator
highlight	mammoth	peacefulness	regiment
hog	marigold	pearl	region
horizontal	marriage	perceive	rejoice
hovercraft	material	perform	relative
humiliating	measurements	period	remedy
hurricane	memorial	permanently	removal
ignorance	memorise	permission	representatives
ignorant	meringue	persist	responsible
impatiently	miaow	personal	rheumatic
improvement	million	perspired	ridiculous
income	miniature	pinafore	rifle
independence	minor	pioneer	roar
individual	misconceive	plane	route
indoors	missing	poison	sacred
influenza	mistletoe	polar	safety
injure	mixture	portion	saxophone
injury	moisture	posture	scene
insert	moo	practical	scenery
insolent	mosque	prayer	scent
instantly	multiplies	prefer	scholar
instruct	natural	preferred	seasoning
instrument	naturally	premature	segment
insult	navigate	priest	sensible
introduction	nervous	production	sentence

Book Ten Word List

shriek
shy
signature
simile
situated
skeleton
skull
sleepiness
soar
soccer
soldier
solution
soup
sown
special
spoor
square-dance
stadium
stage
stagnant
stallion
standard

statement
structure
student
submit
subtract
succeed
success
successful
suffocate
suffocated
suffocating
supersonic
supplying
surely
surface
surrender
surround
taped
telescope
temperate
temperature
temporary

tension
texture
therefore
thieve
thoughtfully
threat
thrifty
thrilling
toga
traitor
treatment
treaty
tremendous
trousers
uncomfortable
unemployed
unequal
uniform
unintelligible
union
unofficial
unsympathetic

upholstery
utmost
vane
various
vehicles
view
visible
volcano
wasp
weapon
weariness
wholesome
wireless
wisdom
witch
wither
woollen
worthy
wretched
wrinkle
zone
zoology

Congratulations!

You have now learnt to spell **4,540** words, know what they mean and how to use them in a sentence.

Now move on to **Book 11** to learn lots more words to add to your word bank total.

Exercise 206a
1) situated
2) perform
3) o'clock
4) safety
5) expense
6) soar
7) expensive
8) ninety
9) uniform
10) cocoa

Exercise 206b
11) Force
12) period
13) skull
14) standard
15) surely
16) roar
17) utmost
18) relative
19) entirely
20) scholar

Exercise 207a
1) naturally
2) annual
3) sleepiness
4) threat
5) surface
6) natural
7) heaviness
8) practical
9) general
10) furnace

Exercise 207b
11) soup
12) weapon
13) cough
14) forehead
15) ounce
16) wasp
17) weariness
18) embrace
19) generally
20) business

Exercise 208a
1) peace
2) sentence
3) appeal
4) million
5) improvement
6) region
7) biscuit
8) colony
9) permission
10) juice

Exercise 208b
11) orphan
12) bicycle
13) abundant
14) geography
15) defence
16) Admission
17) union
18) statement
19) instantly
20) elephant

Crossword No. 206

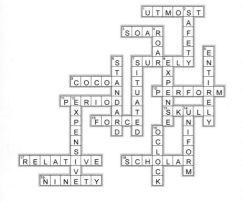

Letter = I

Crossword No. 207

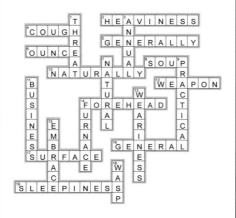

Letter = V

Crossword No. 208

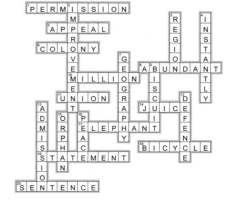

Letter = A

Answers

Exercise 209a

1) laundry
2) view
3) August
4) submit
5) length
6) conductor
7) shriek
8) author
9) priest
10) fierce

Exercise 209b

11) scenery
12) depth
13) scent
14) fault
15) governor
16) scene
17) subtract
18) pause
19) autumn
20) brief

Exercise 210a

1) anxious
2) lungs
3) avoid
4) trousers
5) arouse
6) wither
7) surrender
8) various
9) special
10) palm

Exercise 210b

11) abrupt
12) material
13) fury
14) surround
15) moisture
16) curious
17) glorious
18) rejoice
19) worthy
20) choice

Exercise 211a

1) soldier
2) acre
3) succeed
4) New Zealand
5) zone
6) crooked
7) marriage
8) woollen
9) personal
10) debt

Exercise 211b

11) successful
12) prayer
13) pearl
14) doubt
15) success
16) loose
17) deny
18) machine
19) foolish
20) carriage

Crossword No. 209

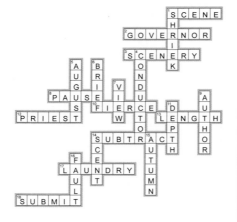

Letter = B

Crossword No. 210

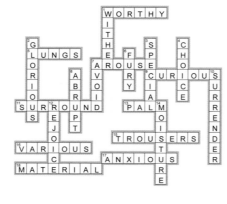

Letter = I

Crossword No. 211

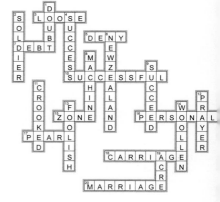

Letter = O

Answers

Exercise 212a

1) festival
2) greet
3) determination
4) majority
5) liberal
6) decrease
7) minor
8) Traitor
9) criminal
10) production

Exercise 212b

11) proportion
12) decline
13) removal
14) determine
15) introduction
16) fund
17) declare
18) portion
19) protection
20) major

Exercise 213a

1) skeleton
2) cushion
3) pioneer
4) Greece
5) instruct
6) announce
7) accurate
8) keen
9) injure
10) engineer

Exercise 213b

11) ghost
12) income
13) career
14) accuse
15) contract
16) addition
17) injury
18) accustom
19) insert
20) insult

Exercise 214a

1) contempt
2) coil
3) wireless
4) conferred
5) prefer
6) therefore
7) grateful
8) lodging
9) poison
10) control

Exercise 214b

11) consent
12) enterprise
13) hesitate
14) wholesome
15) preferred
16) convince
17) grudge
18) conclude
19) condemn
20) wisdom

Crossword No. 212

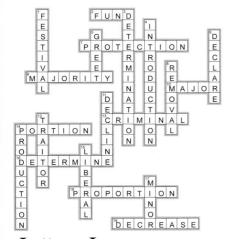

Letter = L

Crossword No. 213

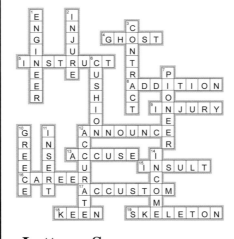

Letter = S

Crossword No. 214

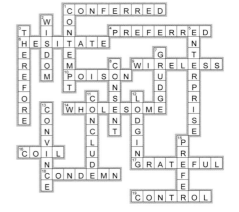

Letter = I

At the Wedding

1. PEW	2. BOOKMARK	3. TAPESTRY	4. CHOIR	5. PILLAR
6. BOW-TIE	7. CANDLE	8. BRIDESMAID	9. SURPLICE	10. ANGEL
11. BRIDEGROOM	12. ARCH	13. BRIDE	14. POSY	15. PULPIT

At the Visit to HMS Victory

1. MIZZEN	2. GAFF	3. PORTHOLES	4. JIB	5. CROW'S-NEST
6. BOLLARD	7. CANNONBALL	8. GANGPLANK	9. BARREL	10. TOPSAIL
11. RIGGING	12. DORY	13. ENSIGN	14. ANCHOR	15. RUDDER

Answers

Exercise 215a

1) delicate
2) confident
3) fragment
4) experiment
5) cement
6) discourage
7) navigate
8) Treaty
9) remedy
10) candidate

Exercise 215b

11) debate
12) student
13) regiment
14) camera
15) stage
16) garage
17) baggage
18) average
19) certificate
20) continent

Exercise 216a

1) volcano
2) puncture
3) route
4) prominent
5) temperate
6) jealous
7) couch
8) tremendous
9) ornament
10) nervous

Exercise 216b

11) recently
12) sensible
13) instrument
14) ridiculous
15) prosperous
16) temperature
17) agriculture
18) treatment
19) lecture
20) Recent

Dickens's Page of Knowledge

1. Orville and Wilbur Wright
   Manned Flight.

2. The Pilgrim Fathers
   Settle America.

3. Sir Edmund Hillary
   Climb Everest.

4. Neil Armstrong
   Moon Walk.

5. Robert Edwin Peary
   North Pole.

6. Captain Matthew Webb
   Swim the Channel.

7. Sir Francis Chichester
   Single-handed around the World.

8. Louis Blériot
   Cross Channel Flight.

9. Roald Amundsen
   South Pole.

10. Yuri Gagarin
    Orbit the Earth.

Crossword No. 215

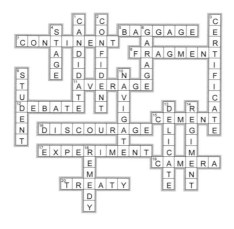

Letter = M

Crossword No. 216

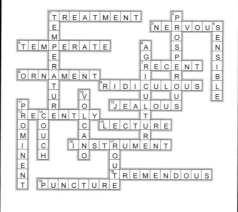

Letter = C

Answers

Exercise 217a
1) telescope
2) rifle
3) ceiling
4) wretched
5) sacred
6) responsible
7) Witch
8) invisible
9) attendance
10) deceitful

Exercise 217b
11) hatred
12) ignorance
13) abundance
14) visible
15) appearance
16) perceive
17) wrinkle
18) deceit
19) earthquake
20) ignorant

Exercise 218a
1) double-bass
2) Euro
3) makeup
4) engagement
5) jodhpurs
6) Bartering
7) crossbow
8) greaseproof
9) heiress
10) librarian

Exercise 218b
11) harp
12) anorak
13) escalator
14) calculator
15) horizontal
16) cashier
17) harass
18) Lavender
19) aviary
20) insolent

Exercise 219a
1) Farenheit
2) nursing
3) bawl
4) exhume
5) embroidery
6) pyjamas
7) unemployed
8) sown
9) Comedy
10) fidget

Exercise 219b
11) blowpipe
12) hovercraft
13) marigold
14) excise
15) fined
16) uncomfortable
17) measurements
18) mistletoe
19) crypt
20) decisions

Crossword No. 217

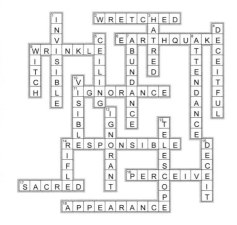

Letter = O

Crossword No. 218

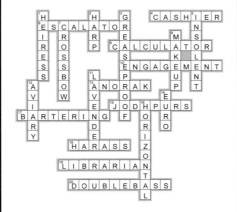

Letter = A

Crossword No. 219

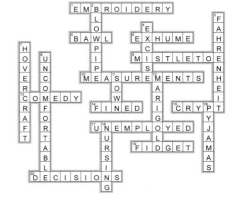

Letter = N

At the Fishmonger's

1. BOATER	2. CASH REGISTER	3. CRABS	4. FINS	5. COUNTER
6. SKELETON	7. LOBSTER	8. SCALES	9. OYSTERS	10. TONGS
11. GALOSHES	12. ICE	13. APRON	14. JAR	15. WRAPPER

At the Recreation Park

1. SKATEBOARD	2. CYCLIST	3. GOALPOST	4. ROLLERBLADES	5. FOOTBALL
6. HOOD	7. RUGBY BALL	8. DECAL	9. RUNNER	10. RAMP
11. SCOOTER	12. TENNIS	13. ACROBAT	14. JOGGER	15. TIER

Answers

Exercise 220a
1) referee
2) fiord
3) rambling
4) mosque
5) benevolent
6) upholstery
7) oasis
8) indoors
9) fiction
10) spoor

Exercise 220b
11) unofficial
12) rapped
13) unequal
14) Pyramid
15) boutique
16) supersonic
17) vane
18) quadrant
19) vehicles
20) influenza

Exercise 221a
1) oast-house
2) *Pauper*
3) unintelligible
4) feminine
5) representative
6) humiliating
7) seasoning
8) radiographer
9) saxophone
10) meringue

Exercise 221b
11) square-dance
12) refrigerator
13) patience
14) rapier
15) rectangle
16) cymbals
17) feint
18) pinafore
19) zoology
20) hurricane

Exercise 222a
1) solution
2) recapitulate
3) polar
4) toga
5) comet
6) soccer
7) mammoth
8) Broccoli
9) segment
10) lasso

Exercise 222b
11) eruption
12) thrilling
13) except
14) plane
15) overtake
16) glimmer
17) unsympathetic
18) actual
19) persist
20) clue

Crossword No. 220

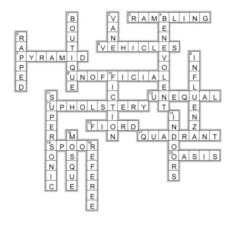

Letter = C

Crossword No. 221

Letter = I

Crossword No. 222

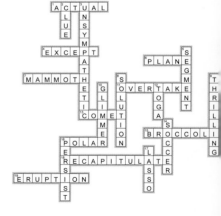

Letter = I

Answers

Exercise 223a
1) commando
2) organise
3) hammock
4) hog
5) overweight
6) fate
7) bouquet
8) excavator
9) annually
10) mixture

Exercise 223b
11) compact
12) completing
13) adore
14) missing
15) structure
16) thrifty
17) bore
18) raccoon
19) perspired
20) radiant

Exercise 224a
1) germ
2) suffocating
3) borderline
4) tension
5) appendix
6) alternative
7) multiplies
8) misconceive
9) crevice
10) bibliography

Exercise 224b
11) memorial
12) combining
13) shy
14) antler
15) premature
16) texture
17) fries
18) expenditure
19) comprehend
20) curiously

Exercise 225a
1) miaow
2) individual
3) coping
4) memorise
5) completed
6) permanently
7) heroine
8) peacefulness
9) comprise
10) defiantly

Exercise 225b
11) suffocate
12) impatiently
13) thoughtfully
14) supplying
15) signature
16) patter
17) admires
18) eventual
19) taped
20) amuses

Crossword No. 223

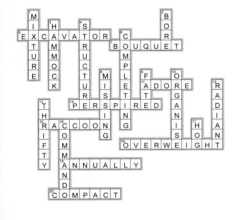

Crossword No. 224

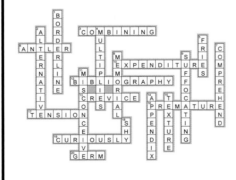

Crossword No. 225

Letter = R

Letter = A

Letter = P

Answers

Exercise 226a

1) suffocated
2) fiend
3) thieve
4) habitual
5) confidential
6) highlight
7) confusion
8) defuses
9) stallion
10) cope

Exercise 226b

11) obediently
12) amaze
13) stagnant
14) amused
15) posture
16) allocating
17) conscientiously
18) miniature
19) excites
20) moo

Crossword No. 226

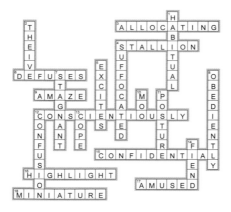

Letter = S

Exercise 227a

1) duvet
2) congeal
3) bistro
4) anticlockwise
5) Rheumatic
6) Exchequer
7) apostrophe
8) temporary
9) documentary
10) coped

Exercise 227b

11) independence
12) Celsius
13) accustomed
14) exorbitant
15) simile
16) antisocial
17) stadium
18) film
19) justification
20) nutritious

Crossword No. 227

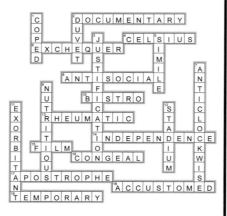

Letter = H

Mystery Word
I V A B I O L
B O L I V I A

Mystery Word
S I M C O A N C
M O C C A S I N

Mystery Word
I I R A P S H
A I R S H I P

PROGRESS CHARTS

Scores

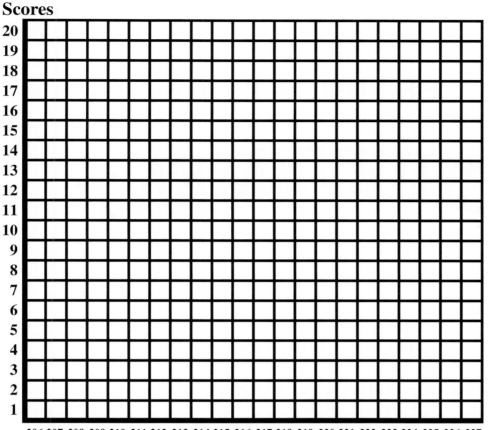

Exercises

Shade in your score for each exercise on the graph. Add them up for your total score out of 460. Ask an adult to work out the percentage.

Total Score

Percentage

 A

Scores

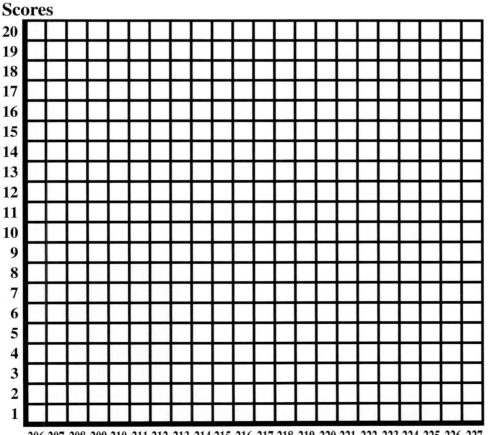

Crosswords

Shade in your score for each crossword on the graph. Add them up for your total score out of 460.

Total Score

Percentage

 B

For the average percentage add %A and %B and divide by 2

Overall Percentage

%

CERTIFICATE OF

ACHIEVEMENT

This certifies

____

has successfully completed

11+ Spelling & Vocabulary

WORKBOOK **10**

Overall percentage score achieved [   ] %

Comment ______________________________

____

Signed ______________________________

(teacher/parent/guardian)

Date ______________________________

SUCCESSFUL ae COMPLETION